THE COMPLETE ORGAN PLAYER
THE CARPENTERS

C000165366

Wise Publications
London/New York/Paris/Sydney/Copenhagen/Madrid

Exclusive Distributors:
Music Sales Limited
8/9 Frith Street, London W1V 5TZ, England.
Music Sales Pty Limited
120 Rothschild Avenue, Rosebery, NSW 2018, Australia.

Order No. AM928411
ISBN 0-7119-4928-X
This book © Copyright 1995 by Wise Publications

Compiled by Peter Evans
Music arranged by Kenneth Baker
Music processed by MSS Studios
Book design by Studio Twenty, London
Cover photograph by London Features International

Printed in the United Kingdom by
J.B. Offset Printers (Marks Tey) Limited, Marks Tey, Essex.

Your Guarantee of Quality
As publishers, we strive to produce every book to
the highest commercial standards.
The music has been freshly engraved and the book has
been carefully designed to minimise awkward page turns
and to make playing from it a real pleasure.
Particular care has been given to specifying acid-free, neutral-sized
paper made from pulps which have not been elemental chlorine bleached.
This pulp is from farmed sustainable forests and was produced with
special regard for the environment.
Throughout, the printing and binding have been planned to ensure a sturdy,
attractive publication which should give years of enjoyment.
If your copy fails to meet our high standards, please inform us
and we will gladly replace it.

Music Sales' complete catalogue describes thousands of titles and is
available in full colour sections by subject, direct from Music Sales Limited.
Please state your areas of interest and send a cheque/postal order for £1.50 for postage to:
Music Sales Limited, Newmarket Road, Bury St. Edmunds, Suffolk IP33 3YB.

An Old Fashioned Love Song 20
Crystal Lullaby 36
Goodbye To Love 34
I Won't Last A Day Without You 16
Jambalaya (On The Bayou) 8
Let Me Be The One 28
Mr Guder 14
One Love 18
Only Yesterday 10
Rainy Days And Mondays 32
Sing 30
Solitaire 24
Superstar 26
(They Long To Be) Close To You 42
Top Of The World 4
We've Only Just Begun 6
Yesterday Once More 39

Chord Charts 45, 46, 47, 48

TOP OF THE WORLD
Words by John Bettis. Music by Richard Carpenter.

Upper: flute
Lower: flutes
Pedal: bass guitar
Drums: 8 beat

stop drums

5

WE'VE ONLY JUST BEGUN

Words by Paul Williams. Music by Roger Nichols.

Upper: string ensemble
Lower: flutes
Pedal: bass guitar
Drums: 8 beat

JAMBALAYA (ON THE BAYOU)

Words & Music by Hank Williams.

Upper: violin
Lower: flutes + piano
Pedal: 8'
Drums: swing

ONLY YESTERDAY

Words by John Bettis. Music by Richard Carpenter.

Upper: oboe
Lower: flutes
Pedal: bass guitar
Drums: 8 beat

MR. GUDER

Words by John Bettis. Music by Richard Carpenter.

Upper: synth.
Lower: flutes + piano
Pedal: bass guitar
Drums: rock

I WON'T LAST A DAY WITHOUT YOU

Words by Paul Williams. Music by Roger Nichols.

Upper: trumpet
Lower: flutes
Pedal: 8'
Drums: 8 beat

ONE LOVE

Words by John Bettis. Music by Richard Carpenter.

Upper: piano
Lower: flutes
Pedal: 8'
Drums: 8 beat

Lyrics:
One love in my young life took me some-where I had ne-ver been, and I want to live a-gain, breathe a-gain in the shel-ter of his bright-ly wo-ven love song. *(Instrumental 2nd time)* So long I have want-ed love to be sit-ting just this near to me. Now my wai-ting heart is free.

* E7, omitting note "D"

AN OLD FASHIONED LOVE SONG

Words & Music by Paul Williams.

Upper: saxophone
Lower: flutes + piano
Pedal: 8'
Drums: swing

CHORUS

23

SOLITAIRE

Words & Music by Philip Cody & Neil Sedaka.

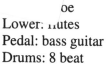

Lower: flutes
Pedal: bass guitar
Drums: 8 beat

ev - 'ry road that takes him, takes him down. while life goes on a - round him e - v'ry-

where, he's pla - ying so - li - taire. But

kee - ping to him - self, be - gins to deal, and still the king of hearts is well con-

cealed. A - no - ther lo - sing game comes to an end, and he deals them

1. out a - gain. Upper: cut strings

2. out a - gain. *mp*

25

SUPERSTAR

Words & Music by Leon Russell & Bonnie Bramlett.

JO
11th MARCH
2002

Upper: guitar
Lower: flutes
Pedal: bass guitar
Drums: 16 beat

27

LET ME BE THE ONE

Words by Paul Williams. Music by Roger Nichols.

Upper: piano
Lower: flutes
Pedal: bass guitar
Drums: 8 beat

Lyrics:

Some sleep-less night, if you should find your-self a-lone.
To set things right, when this old world's turned up-side down.

Let me be the one — you run to, let me be the one — you come to when you need some-one to turn to. Let me be the one.

For love and un-der-stand-ing, to find a qui-et

* F♯m7, with pedal A

SING

Words & Music by Joe Raposo.

Upper: vibraphone
Lower: flutes
Pedal: bass guitar
Drums: 8 beat

RAINY DAYS AND MONDAYS

Words by Paul Williams. Music by Roger Nichols.

Upper: human voice
Lower: flutes
Pedal: bass guitar
Drums: 8 beat

GOODBYE TO LOVE

Words by John Bettis. Music by Richard Carpenter.

Lower: flutes
Pedal: bass guitar
Drums: 8 beat

CRYSTAL LULLABY

Words by John Bettis. Music by Richard Carpenter.

Upper: celeste (or vibraphone)
Lower: flutes
Pedal: 8'
Drums: 8 beat

YESTERDAY ONCE MORE

Words & Music by Richard Carpenter & John Bettis.

Upper: trumpet
Lower: flutes
Pedal: bass guitar
Drums: 8 beat

(THEY LONG TO BE) CLOSE TO YOU

Words by Hal David. Music by Burt Bacharach.

Upper: vibraphone
Lower: flutes + piano
Pedal: 8'
Drums: swing

44

CHORD CHARTS (For Left Hand)

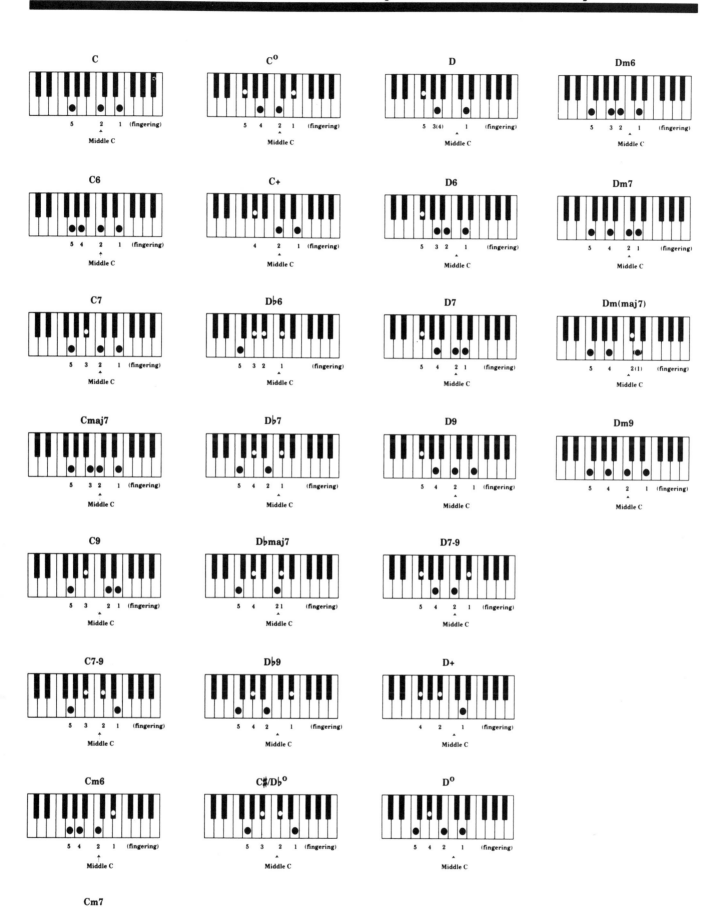

CHORD CHARTS (For Left Hand)

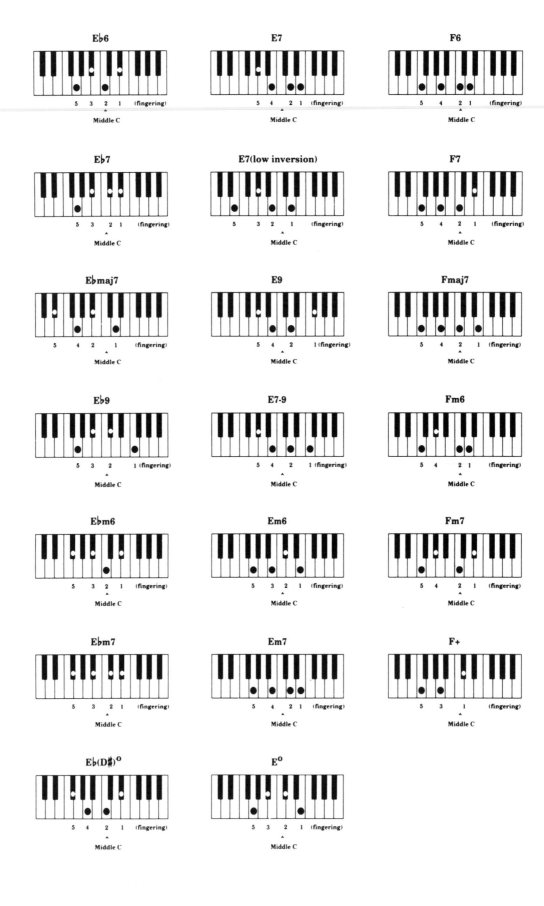

CHORD CHARTS (For Left Hand)

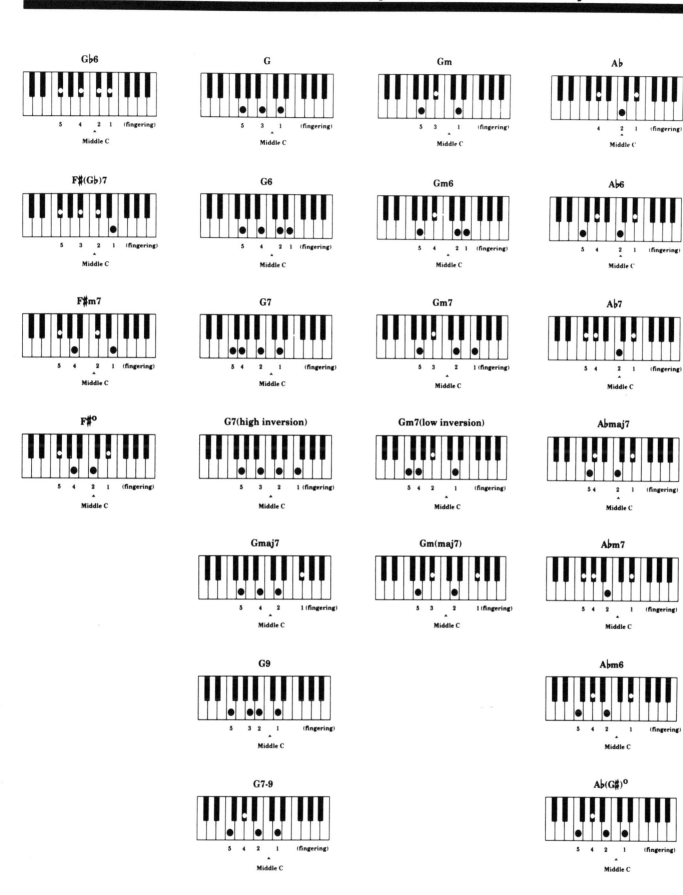

CHORD CHARTS (For Left Hand)

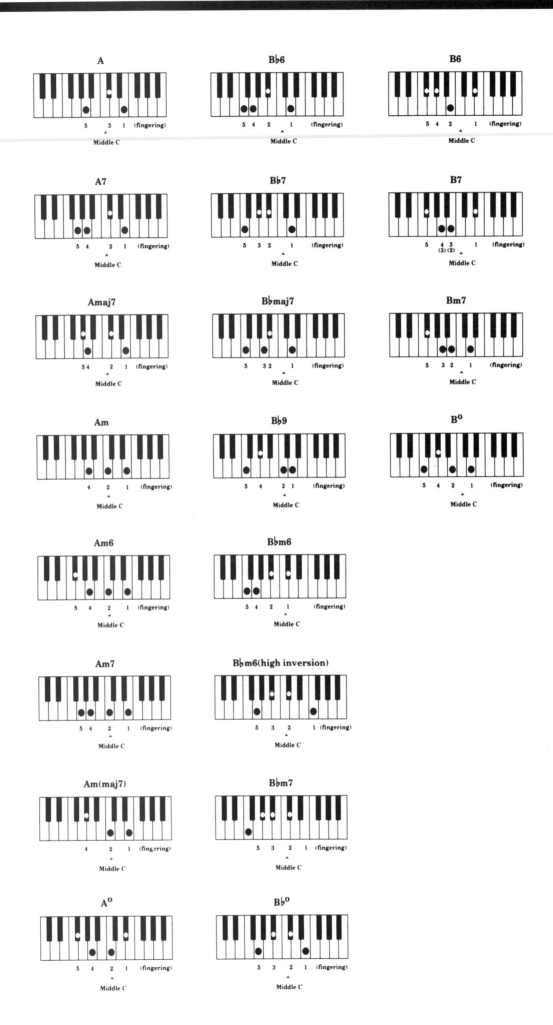